FIND THE
Journeys around the
WORLD

Written by
David Long

Illustrated by
Andy Rowland

chartwell
books

As you journey through the pages of this book, you'll explore real places from the ancient world, learn what life was like for these ancient civilizations, and find out about some of the key moments in ancient world history in the minutest of detail.

Meet the Egyptians who built towering pyramids filled with glorious treasures, travel to the Kingdom of Kush and uncover how it grew rich by mining iron and gold, and learn how the Greeks fought the fiercest sea battles of the ancient world.

After so many centuries, it can be hard to know exactly when an ancient civilization began or ended. The end could be quite sudden, for example when one group or tribe was conquered by another. But a new civilization can take years or even decades to develop. It is normal to provide a range of dates to explain roughly when a particular civilization existed, because modern historians cannot be more accurate than this.

HOW TO USE THIS BOOK

Turn the page and soak up the action before your eyes. Each time you revisit a scene, you'll see something new! Read the text and find out what's happening. Which Aztec is playing a pounding beat on the drums? Can you spot the Roman soldier preparing for battle? Can you see Olmec people praying to their great big stone gods?

Next, see if you can spot the 10 items described on each page. Take a close look at each action-packed scene and cutaway illustration. You'll find so many treasures in every eyeboggling illustration, each described down to the tiniest detail.

Now turn to page 38 and test your memory. Can you remember where you saw each item? If not, don't worry! Go back for one more explore-and-find adventure. You're bound to spot much more this time around. Lastly, learn all about a host of important people from throughout these ancient civilizations on page 36, and then turn to page 46 to study the timeline.

What are you waiting for? Discover the secrets of the ancient world!

CONTENTS

MESOPOTAMIA (C. 5000 – C. 500 BC)

Mesopotamia means "between two rivers" and it was the name given to the area lying to the east of the Mediterranean Sea. The two rivers were the Tigris and the Euphrates and the land between them is sometimes called "the cradle of civilization." Today it is now parts of Iraq, Iran, Syria, and Turkey.

It was here that some of the first cities were built, usually around large temples, and each city had its own ruler. Archaeologists believe that some of the cities in this area shared the same script for writing, but they had different languages and laws. They also had different names for the many gods that were worshipped in the temples.

Men and women both worked and were mostly treated as equals. This was unusual in the ancient world but produced some of the most important inventions in history.

10 THINGS TO SPOT

WHEEL The wheel was invented in Mesopotamia around 3500 BC. It was used by potters to begin with and it was years before anyone thought of attaching one to a cart or chariot.

WRITING The earliest form of writing came from Mesopotamia and it was a complicated script called "cuneiform." It took 12 years to learn how to use it!

SCRIBES Rulers and powerful priests employed scribes who could read and write cuneiform. Only the very rich could afford to send their children to the schools where these skills were taught.

CHANNELS Farmers dug narrow channels from rivers to bring water to their fields. This sort of irrigation made agriculture much more productive.

ARD This was a kind of plow pulled by oxen, which enabled Mesopotamians to grow more crops than they needed. The rest were sold to make money.

SEXAGESIMAL Selling was so important that people needed to have a reliable counting system. "Sexagesimal" was a counting system that used 12 knuckles on one hand and five fingers on the other.

TIME Mesopotamian ideas about time led to an hour being divided into 60 minutes, and a minute being divided into 60 seconds.

SAILING BOATS The first boats appeared in Mesopotamia around 5,000 years ago. They had square sails, were slow, and could only travel in the direction of the wind. However, these boats made it easier to trade between different cities.

NINKASI Mesopotamian women could own their own businesses, and many of the first beer and winemakers were women. There was a goddess of beer, called Ninkasi, and people drank beer through long straws.

CLAY TABLETS The world's oldest piece of literature is a poem called *The Epic of Gilgamesh*. It was written down by a Mesopotamian scribe on clay tablets more than 4,000 years ago.

INDUS VALLEY CIVILIZATION (C. 4000 – 1500 BC)

This huge area is where India and Pakistan are found today. It developed from small farming communities along the Indus river into hundreds of towns and several large, walled cities. Occupying around 450,000 square miles, the Indus Valley was far larger than Egypt and Mesopotamia, the other two great ancient civilizations.

The people here were the first to make bricks. They did this by taking clay from the banks of the river and baking it to make it hard. These bricks were then used to build the cities of Harappa and Mohenjo-daro which were home to tens of thousands of people. Narrow streets were laid out in an orderly plan around a building called the "citadel." This was on top of a high earth mound and contained public baths, meeting places, and possibly large storehouses for keeping food.

10 THINGS TO SPOT

 HOUSES The largest houses had internal courtyards and private wells. Even small ones included drainage systems and bathrooms so they must have been relatively comfortable for the time.

 LAMPS Lamps made of seashells were filled with oil or animal fat to light the houses after dark.

 BITUMEN Builders used fires to heat a natural tar-like substance called "bitumen." This was used as mortar to stick bricks together and to make baths and pools waterproof.

 WORKSHOPS Small workshops located on the grid of narrow streets housed potters' kilns, metalworkers, stone carvers, bead and bangle makers, and vats for dying cloth.

Because no great palaces have ever been found here it is possible there wasn't a powerful king or one single ruler. Some historians think that instead of the rich controlling the poor, this might have been a society in which everyone was considered equal.

 FISH-HOOKS Copper and bronze were used to make fish-hooks so fish must have formed part of the Indus diet.

 FARMERS Farming was an important activity. Farmers grew wheat, barley, peas, and dates as well as keeping cattle, chickens, pigs, camels, and possibly even elephants. Dogs and monkeys were kept as pets.

 FOOD Food was supplied to the towns and cities in exchange for manufactured goods such as tools, cooking pots, cotton clothing, and colored beads.

 JEWELRY Jewelry and other luxury items were often made of ivory. Gold, silver, and copper came from mines in what is now Afghanistan. Other imports included precious stones such as lapis lazuli, turquoise, and fuchsite.

 WRITING The people of the Indus Valley had their own form of writing. Thousands of examples have been found on pots, stone tablets, and carved seals. It is very complex and to this day is still not fully understood.

 GODS Not much is known about the local religions but images have been discovered of a godlike figure with a human face, an elephant's trunk, a tiger's body, and the legs of a bull.

10 THINGS TO SPOT

 PYRAMIDS There are almost 140 pyramids in Egypt. The tallest is the Pyramid of Khufu which, at 481 feet, held the record as the world's tallest building for an amazing 3,800 years!

 WORKERS Each pyramid took thousands of workers many years to complete. Because of this, work on a new one often started when a young pharaoh came to the throne.

 MUMMIES Before a pharaoh's body could be buried, it was mummified. This involved removing most of the organs (the brain was pulled out through the nose!) and covering the body in salt for 40 days to dry it out.

 SARCOPHAGUS The dried body was then wrapped in long strips of linen and put in a wooden coffin, which was painted to look like the dead person. This was then placed in a larger stone coffin called a sarcophagus.

EGYPT (3100 – 525 BC)

Established along the banks of the mighty river Nile in North Africa, ancient Egypt was a rich and powerful civilization which lasted for around 3,000 years. Much of its success depended on the river Nile flooding every year, which created excellent farmland. The Egyptians became experts at growing crops needed to feed a large population. Fishermen and traders also worked on the Nile, traveling in boats made of reeds.

Egypt's most famous monuments are its vast pyramids, which were built as tombs for the rulers, known as pharaohs. The Pyramid of Khufu was the largest and weighs over six million tons!

Egyptians believed that the dead went to an afterlife. The pyramids were designed with secret passageways and chambers which contained food, clothes, gold, and treasure for the pharaoh to enjoy after his death.

THIEVES! Thieves often broke into the pyramids to steal gold and other treasures. This was such a serious crime that anyone caught doing it was punished by being put to death.

SHIPS The Egyptians were expert shipbuilders. A whole ship was buried next to King Khufu's pyramid for him to use in the afterlife. Today it is one of the oldest, largest, and best-preserved vessels from any ancient civilization.

 TOOTHPASTE Tiny pieces of grit and sand in Egyptian bread caused lots of dental problems, so the Egyptians invented the first toothpaste. This contained salt, pepper, mint, and dried iris (a type of flower).

MAKEUP Egyptian men and women both wore makeup which they thought had magical healing powers. It was made of soot and ground-up rock.

 PEPI II Pepi II was a six-year-old pharaoh who hated flies! He told his slaves to cover themselves in honey in the hope that it would keep the annoying insects away from him.

SPHINX As tall as a seven-story building, the Sphinx is one of the world's largest pieces of carved stone. It has the head of a human and the body of a lion. Part of its nose is missing, and even today no-one knows what happened to it!

OLMEC (1600 – 350 BC)

The Olmecs established Central America's first civilization in what is now Mexico. Most people lived in small farming settlements but over time cities grew up around temples and ceremonial or religious sites at San Lorenzo Tenochtitlán and La Venta.

A high clay mound at La Venta, which faces north towards the Pole Star, is known as the Great Temple. People think that the position of the Great Temple means that Olmec priests must have studied the stars and had some understanding of astronomy. Tall pillars, thrones, and gigantic stone heads were placed at the bottom of the mound. These were carved from heavy blocks of stone which must have been carried down from the mountains. No-one knows how this was done or what language the people spoke.

10 THINGS TO SPOT

 FOREST FIRES The Olmec practiced a sort of farming called "slash-and-burn." Forests were cleared by setting fire to bushes and trees. The ash left behind was used as fertilizer to help grow crops such as beans and corn.

 ALLIGATORS Alligators and turtles living in the swamps were caught, cooked, and eaten.

 GODS Many different gods were worshipped. These may have included jaguars, feathered snakes, and a type of dragon with a forked tongue.

GRINDING STONES Stones for grinding corn were made from volcanic rock because it is a very hardwearing material.

ROCK HEADS The Olmec's most famous monuments are giant carved heads made from blocks of volcanic rock called basalt.

 MOSAICS Decorated mosaics covered many square feet. These were created using hundreds of pieces of hard, green serpentine rock.

 PRECIOUS STONES The dead were often buried with precious items made of jade, pyrite, obsidian, and other stones, which the Olmec considered more valuable than gold.

 BALL GAMES A popular game was played with a solid ball of rubber. Players probably hit this with their hips, but no-one is quite sure what the rules were.

 CARVINGS Most carvings were of gods, men, and strange animals, but a few have been discovered showing girls or women and even a baby.

 VOLCANOES No-one knows why the Olmec died out. One theory is that volcanic eruptions led to climate change and ruined the soil needed to grow food.

So far only a few examples have been found of Olmec writing. These use small symbols or pictures and are the oldest form of writing ever discovered in the Western Hemisphere.

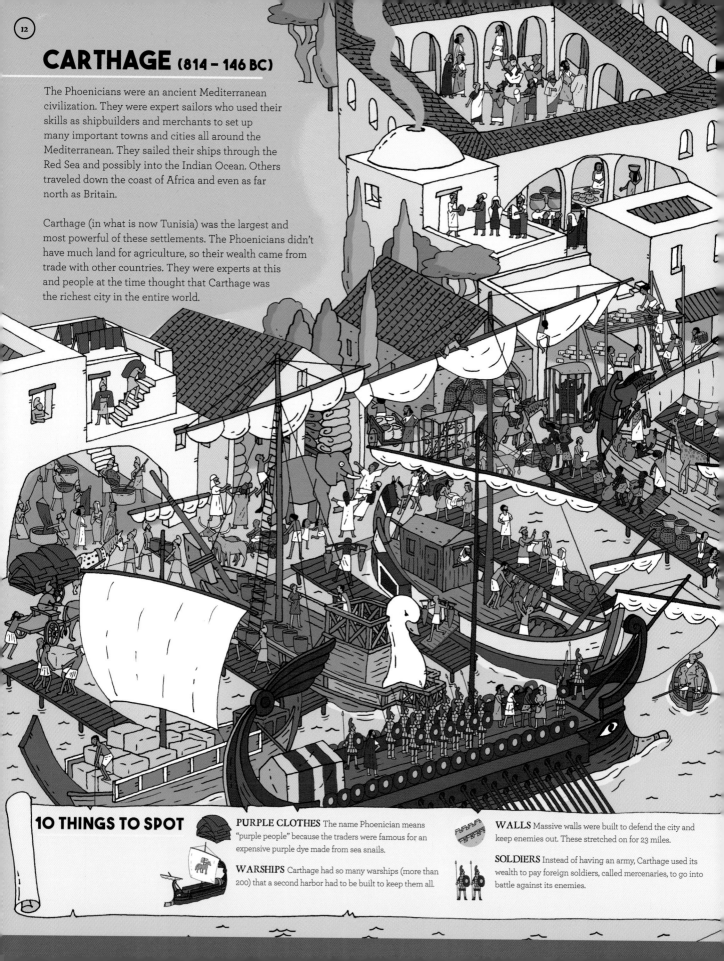

CARTHAGE (814 – 146 BC)

The Phoenicians were an ancient Mediterranean civilization. They were expert sailors who used their skills as shipbuilders and merchants to set up many important towns and cities all around the Mediterranean. They sailed their ships through the Red Sea and possibly into the Indian Ocean. Others traveled down the coast of Africa and even as far north as Britain.

Carthage (in what is now Tunisia) was the largest and most powerful of these settlements. The Phoenicians didn't have much land for agriculture, so their wealth came from trade with other countries. They were experts at this and people at the time thought that Carthage was the richest city in the entire world.

10 THINGS TO SPOT

PURPLE CLOTHES The name Phoenician means "purple people" because the traders were famous for an expensive purple dye made from sea snails.

WARSHIPS Carthage had so many warships (more than 200) that a second harbor had to be built to keep them all.

WALLS Massive walls were built to defend the city and keep enemies out. These stretched on for 23 miles.

SOLDIERS Instead of having an army, Carthage used its wealth to pay foreign soldiers, called mercenaries, to go into battle against its enemies.

People traded goods including wood, furs, textiles, papyrus, metals, spices, and a special purple dye made from sea snails. This was very expensive because it took thousands of snails to produce a single gram. As a result, purple clothes were mostly worn by kings and emperors.

BRICKS Bricks made of dried earth or "adobe" were used for houses. This was strong enough for some homes to be several stories high.

AGORA The Agora was a central area for political and religious ceremonies. It was also a place for traders to meet and discuss business.

TIN Tin was imported from Britain to make bronze goods. Carthaginians tried to keep this secret so they could sell it at a higher price to other countries.

TRANSLATORS Many different nationalities came to Carthage. Translators were employed to help them communicate with each other.

SLAVES Prisoners captured in war were brought back to Carthage to work as slaves.

URNS The dead were often burned or cremated. Their remains were buried in pots called cremation urns.

KINGDOM OF KUSH (C. 800 BC – 350 AD)

Nubia or the Kingdom of Kush was situated in north-east Africa in what is now Sudan. The kingdom grew rich by mining iron and gold, and by trading ivory, incense, ostrich feathers, and slaves with neighboring countries. Wealth meant power and in the 750s BC, Kashta, the king of Kush, successfully invaded a large part of Egypt. The Kushites controlled this area for the next hundred years.

10 THINGS TO SPOT

 ARCHERS The archers in the Kushite army were so skilled that the kingdom was sometimes called the "Land of the Bow."

 OSTRICHES Ostriches were hunted using bows and arrows. Their feathers were very valuable.

 CAMELS Camels were kept for food long before they were used for transportation.

 QUEENS Many Kushite leaders were women. Queens were called "candace" meaning "sister."

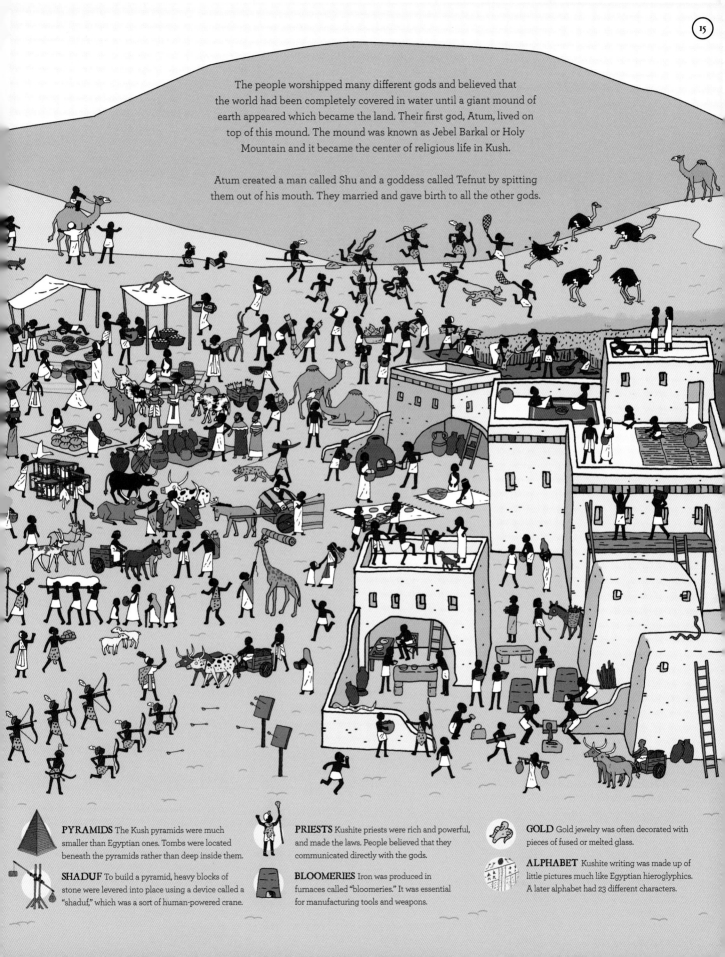

The people worshipped many different gods and believed that the world had been completely covered in water until a giant mound of earth appeared which became the land. Their first god, Atum, lived on top of this mound. The mound was known as Jebel Barkal or Holy Mountain and it became the center of religious life in Kush.

Atum created a man called Shu and a goddess called Tefnut by spitting them out of his mouth. They married and gave birth to all the other gods.

PYRAMIDS The Kush pyramids were much smaller than Egyptian ones. Tombs were located beneath the pyramids rather than deep inside them.

SHADUF To build a pyramid, heavy blocks of stone were levered into place using a device called a "shaduf," which was a sort of human-powered crane.

PRIESTS Kushite priests were rich and powerful, and made the laws. People believed that they communicated directly with the gods.

BLOOMERIES Iron was produced in furnaces called "bloomeries." It was essential for manufacturing tools and weapons.

GOLD Gold jewelry was often decorated with pieces of fused or melted glass.

ALPHABET Kushite writing was made up of little pictures much like Egyptian hieroglyphics. A later alphabet had 23 different characters.

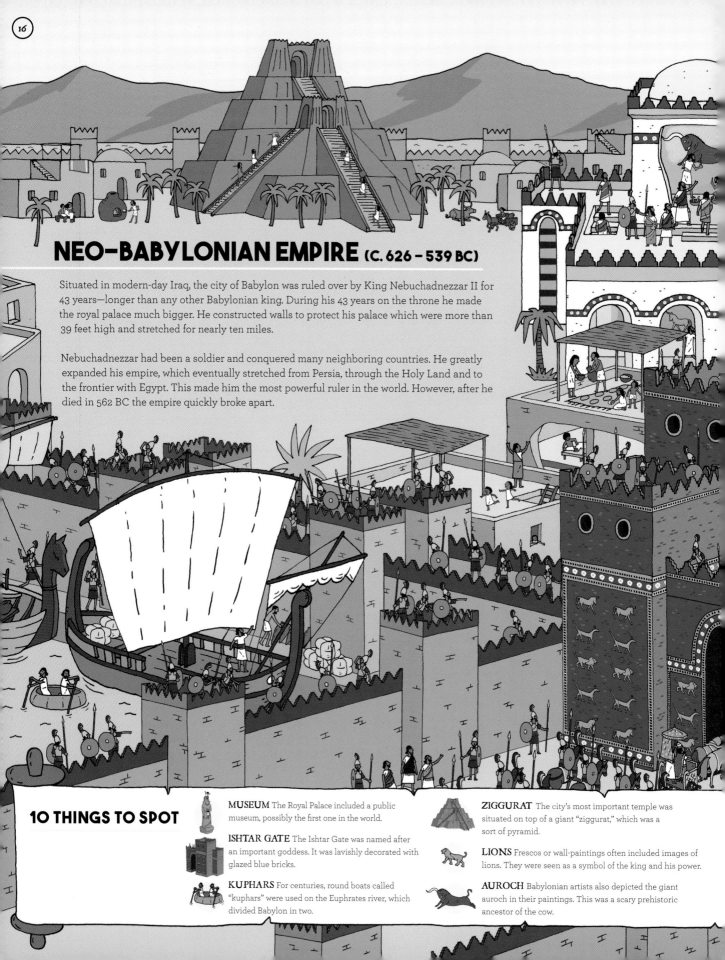

NEO-BABYLONIAN EMPIRE (C. 626 – 539 BC)

Situated in modern-day Iraq, the city of Babylon was ruled over by King Nebuchadnezzar II for 43 years—longer than any other Babylonian king. During his 43 years on the throne he made the royal palace much bigger. He constructed walls to protect his palace which were more than 39 feet high and stretched for nearly ten miles.

Nebuchadnezzar had been a soldier and conquered many neighboring countries. He greatly expanded his empire, which eventually stretched from Persia, through the Holy Land and to the frontier with Egypt. This made him the most powerful ruler in the world. However, after he died in 562 BC the empire quickly broke apart.

10 THINGS TO SPOT

MUSEUM The Royal Palace included a public museum, possibly the first one in the world.

ISHTAR GATE The Ishtar Gate was named after an important goddess. It was lavishly decorated with glazed blue bricks.

KUPHARS For centuries, round boats called "kuphars" were used on the Euphrates river, which divided Babylon in two.

ZIGGURAT The city's most important temple was situated on top of a giant "ziggurat," which was a sort of pyramid.

LIONS Frescos or wall-paintings often included images of lions. They were seen as a symbol of the king and his power.

AUROCH Babylonian artists also depicted the giant auroch in their paintings. This was a scary prehistoric ancestor of the cow.

Nebuchadnezzar's most famous project was the Hanging Gardens of Babylon. These were one of the Seven Wonders of the Ancient World, although archaeologists are still searching for their remains.

CLAY Most buildings were made out of clay rather than stone. Wet clay from the river was pressed into blocks and then baked hard in the sun.

MARDUK The Babylonians' most important god was Marduk who was often shown with Mušḫuššu, his pet dragon.

LANGUAGES Ordinary people spoke Aramaic but the ruling class preferred a much older language called Akkadian. This was written on clay tablets using a complicated cuneiform script.

CRAFTSMEN Craftsmen were not slaves but instead were free men. They were well-paid for producing elaborate stone carvings and gold jewelry.

PERSIAN EMPIRE (C. 553 – 330 BC)

Around 2,500 years ago, the Persian Empire was the largest empire ever seen. Covering 2.1 million square miles, it was created by one powerful king and destroyed by another more than two centuries later.
Its creator was Cyrus the Great who had many conquests under his belt, which made him the ruler of a lot of the ancient world.

Centered on what is now Iran (but stretching across parts of Europe, Africa, and India) the Persian Empire was home to millions of people with many different religions and cultures. Cyrus introduced an official language to bring all these cultures together and kept a large army to ensure he remained in power. He organized a network of new roads and a postal system to provide efficient links between his four capital cities.

Cyrus was an impressive leader, but when he died the empire fell into chaos because of weaker rulers. In 330 BC it was invaded by the Greek military commander, Alexander the Great.

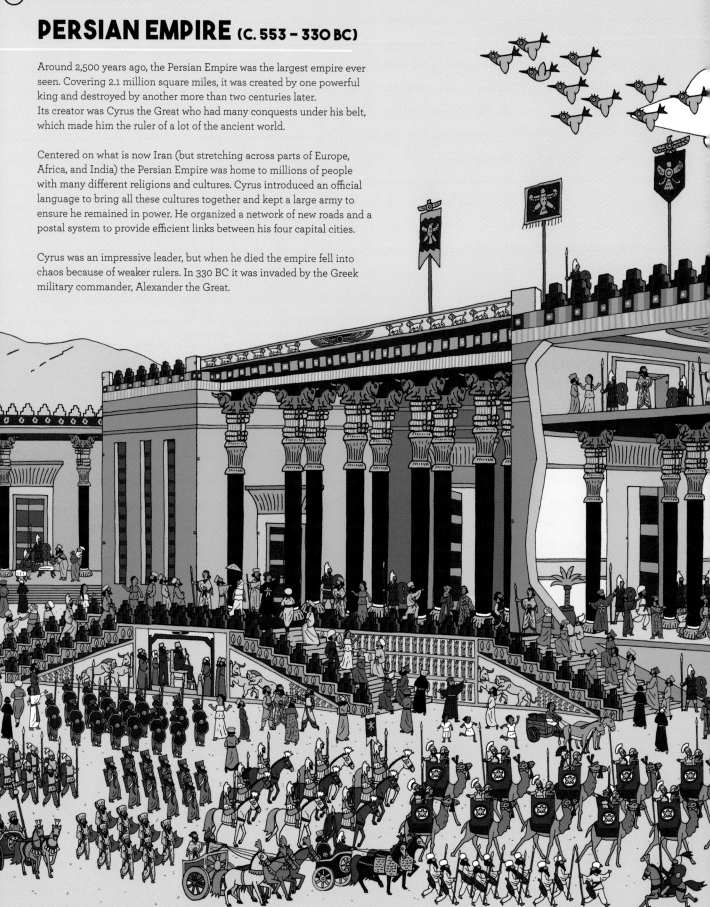

10 THINGS TO SPOT

ARMY The Persian army recruited soldiers of many different races.

CAMELS AND HORSES Armed troops rode camels into battle as well as horses.

RELIGION The main religion was Zoroastrianism. However, conquered tribes were allowed to worship their own gods.

MESSENGERS Fast messengers on horseback carried important royal commands around the empire.

SATRAPS The king appointed local rulers called "satraps" to collect taxes and to keep law and order in far-flung parts of the empire.

SPIES The satraps were not always trusted, so the king also employed spies to keep an eye on them.

CRAFTSMEN Artists and craftsmen from different territories created a richly varied Persian style. Luxuries included handwoven carpets and gold statuettes.

RELIEFS Important buildings incorporated ornate, carved-stone panels called "reliefs."

COLUMNS Architectural pillars and columns were more elaborate than anything seen before.

RESERVOIRS To prevent cities from flooding, the Persians built stone reservoirs. These collected the melting snow as it flowed down from the mountains.

10 THINGS TO SPOT

OARSMEN The oarsmen sat in three rows, one above the other.

PROW The front or "prow" of each ship was fitted with a heavy metal structure, which was used to ram enemy vessels.

SWIMMING Most sailors couldn't swim and drowned if their ship was attacked and sunk.

GREEK FIRE Greek fire was a deadly chemical mixture. It was set alight and then sprayed onto the enemy's wooden deck.

SHEARING Another important tactic was "shearing." This meant using the long wooden oars to break the oars of the enemy and injure the oarsmen.

GREECE (550 – 31 BC)

The ancient Greeks are famous for their art, architecture, and great learning. They organized the first ever Olympic Games, invented the idea of democracy, and made many important discoveries in medicine, mathematics, astronomy, and philosophy. They were also great warriors and built a large and well-equipped navy to conquer neighboring cities and to defend their own.

The most important warships used by the ancient Greeks were called "triremes." These had oars as well as sails, which made them fast and highly maneuverable. Hundreds were built with up to 180 oarsmen on each one. These oarsmen were fit and strong professionals who were well paid.

KYBERNETES Changing direction was the job of the helmsman or "kybernetes." Steering oars were located at the back of the vessel.

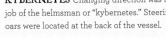 **SAILS** Sails were not used in battle because they were easily damaged.

 IRON HANDS If two ships got close enough, "iron hands" were used to stop the enemy rowing away. These sharp metal hooks were thrown onto the enemy ship, allowing Greek soldiers to leap on to the enemy's deck to fight the crew.

 SHIPS The ships were made for fighting battles. No-one lived onboard and at night sailors slept on land.

 BEACH FIGHTS If ships ran aground during a battle, their crews would continue fighting on the beach.

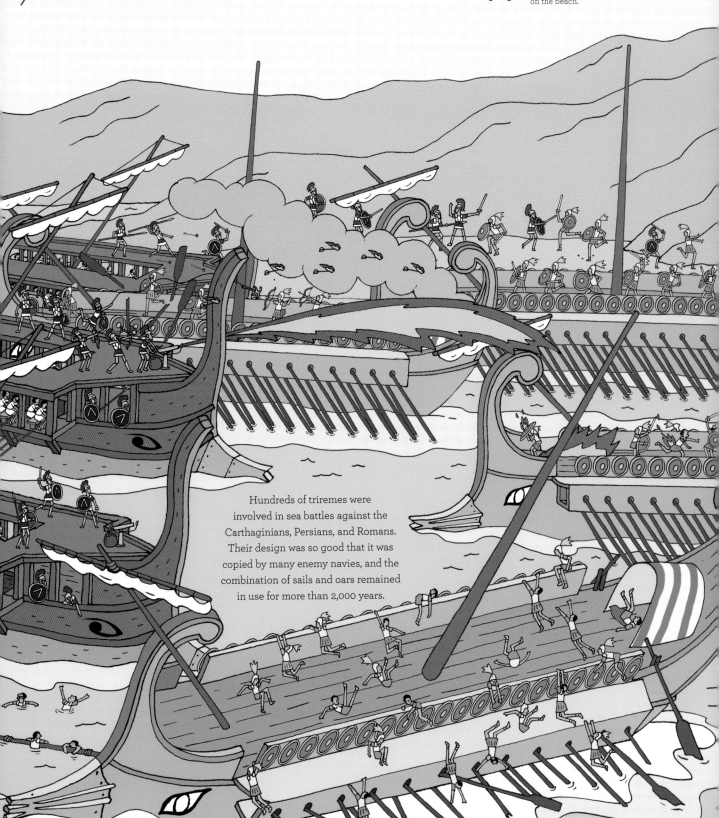

Hundreds of triremes were involved in sea battles against the Carthaginians, Persians, and Romans. Their design was so good that it was copied by many enemy navies, and the combination of sails and oars remained in use for more than 2,000 years.

QIN DYNASTY (221 – 206 BC)

The Qin Dynasty only lasted for 15 years, but it introduced a system of government that lasted for more than 2,000. Its great leader was Qin Shi Huang, whose name means "First Emperor." He was only 13 when he came to the throne but went on to conquer six neighboring kingdoms and create the vast country that we call China.

Each kingdom had different laws, languages, cultures, coins, customs, and even calendars. Qin got rid of them all and introduced new, official ones to unify his mighty empire. He also banned religion so that people would be loyal to him instead of to their gods.

10 THINGS TO SPOT

 BOOKS Emperor Qin ordered all books to be burned unless they were about farming, medicine, or the stars.

 THE GREAT WALL The Great Wall was built to keep out warlike tribes in the north. Eventually it stretched for more than 13,000 miles. That's farther than England to Australia!

SLAVES Most building work was done by slaves, including thousands of convicts and prisoners of war.

ROADS Miles of new roads were created with a central lane. Only the emperor and officials could use this.

CART AXLES On smaller roads, a law required cart axles to be the same size so two could pass by easily.

 TABLETS Qin had stone tablets erected around the country with inscriptions describing his intelligence and achievements.

 UMBRELLA The umbrella was a Chinese invention and first appeared around this time.

 **KITES** The first kites were used by the army to send messages over long distances.

 SWORDS Chinese warriors had iron swords which were much stronger than the bronze ones used by their enemies.

STATUES Captured weapons were often melted down and turned into statues.

Qin wanted to live forever and sought out magicians that would be able to create secret formulas he could drink to make him immortal. But of course, this didn't work. When he died he was buried in a gigantic tomb with his famous terracotta army—8,000 life-size clay warriors, horses, and chariots.

XIONGNU EMPIRE (209 BC – 46 AD)

The Xiongnu Empire occupied large parts of northern China, Mongolia, and Siberia. It was formed when several tribes of nomadic people came together under a powerful ruler called Modu.

Nomads like the Xiongnu spent their lives moving from place to place. They did this to follow the animals they hunted for food, or to move their own herds to areas with richer pastures for grazing. This meant the Xiongnu didn't build any great cities, but eventually they controlled an area almost the size of Europe, much of which was grassland. With a huge army of skilled archers on horseback, Modu was able to conquer many of his neighbors during a reign that lasted more than 30 years.

10 THINGS TO SPOT

 WIVES The chanyu had several wives all at the same time.

 HORSES Horses were very important to the Xiongnu and most warriors had a favorite. White horses were even considered to be sacred.

 GERS Xiongnu families lived in "gers." These were a type of circular tent made from thick felt.

 GAZELLE The Mongolian gazelle was one of the few large animals that could survive in this cold, dry climate, and was hunted for food.

Modu seized power after killing his father. He shot him with an arrow while they were out hunting, and pretended it was an accident. As ruler he was known as "chanyu" meaning "son of Heaven."

 EAGLES Eagles were used for hunting smaller mammals such as lemmings and marmots.

DEFENSES The Chinese built defenses against Modu and his warriors which eventually became the Great Wall of China.

 ROBBERS Warriors often attacked and robbed merchants traveling on the Silk Roads, an important trade route between Europe and Asia.

 KURGANS Xiongnu tombs were hidden beneath earth mounds called "kurgans."

 ROCK CARVINGS A few symbols have been found carved on rocks but it is not known what languages were spoken across the empire.

 GEESE High-flying wild geese were sometimes captured and eaten!

PARTHIAN EMPIRE (247 BC – 224 AD)

The Parthian Empire survived for around 500 years, which was far longer than many other ancient civilizations. Covering more than one million square miles, it stretched northwards from Iran and Iraq, into Turkey, and even parts of Pakistan. This meant the population included people from lots of different cultures and religions. Because of this, Parthian art and architecture were varied and hugely influenced by the styles of their neighbors like Greece and Rome.

The ruler, known as the King of Kings, was rich and powerful. The survival of his empire depended on mounting successful military campaigns against many different invading armies. However, the Parthians also made peaceful alliances with some of their neighbors.

The main trading routes between Asia and Europe crossed the empire. It grew rich on the profits made from luxury goods passing through its territory. These included spices from India that were so expensive that most ordinary people had never seen pepper, let alone tasted it!

10 THINGS TO SPOT

 CATAPHRACTS Many of the Parthian Empire's victories in battle relied on "cataphracts." These were heavily armored horsemen equipped with long, sharp lances (a long pole with a pointed tip).

 THE PARTHIAN SHOT Skilled archers practised something called the Parthian Shot. This involved galloping away from the enemy while firing an arrow backwards.

 SILK Rich Parthians loved silk. However, this had to be imported from China because, for hundreds of years, no-one else knew how to make it.

 EXOTIC LUXURIES In exchange for silk the Parthians supplied the Chinese with other exotic luxuries, such as Roman glass and ostrich eggs.

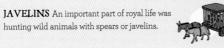 **TAXES** Merchants traveling on the empire's roads had to pay taxes, which made the Parthians even richer.

 JAVELINS An important part of royal life was hunting wild animals with spears or javelins.

BIRDS OF PREY Smaller species such as pheasants and hares were killed using hawks or falcons.

ROYAL GIFTS Lions and stags were sometimes captured and presented as gifts to visiting royalty.

 GŌSĀNĀN Most people couldn't read, so traveling poet-musicians called "gōsānān" entertained them by playing and telling stories.

 ZOROASTRIAN A white belt indicated that the man wearing it was a Zoroastrian, one of the main religions of the empire.

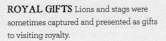

ROMAN EMPIRE (27 BC – 476 AD)

The Roman Empire was the world's most powerful empire. Roman soldiers were heavily armed and well trained. Beginning in what is now Italy, they conquered all the lands around the Mediterranean, much of the Middle East, and most of Britain.

Romans spoke Latin, which eventually developed into the languages that many Europeans speak today. We also use the Roman calendar (which divided the year into 365 days) and July is named after an important Roman ruler: Julius Caesar. He called himself "ruler for life" in 44 BC, but was murdered that same year.

10 THINGS TO SPOT

ROUND ARCHES Round arches are stronger than square doorways and enabled Romans to build much taller buildings than before.

AQUEDUCTS Some of the tallest buildings were "aqueducts" which were used to carry fresh water into Roman towns and cities. The longest one was more than 80 miles in length.

INSULAE The Romans were the first people to live in apartment blocks. These were called "insulae."

SEWERS Huge stone sewers carried waste out of Roman towns.

CONCRETE Romans invented a form of concrete so strong that many buildings are still standing more than 2,000 years later.

CENTRAL HEATING The Romans also invented central heating. Hot air from fires was blown into a space beneath the floor to keep houses warm during the winter.

BALLISTA Roman soldiers were well trained and used weapons like the "ballista." This was a giant catapult used for hurling heavy stones at the walls of enemy cities.

TESTUDO Troops fought in a testudo, a close formation of men who protected themselves from attack by arranging their wooden and leather shields to form walls and a roof.

ROADS Roads were built to move troops around quickly and efficiently.

BIG BEASTS Public entertainment was often very cruel. Thousands of captured wild animals, such as bears, lions, bulls, and even elephants, were made to fight in front of huge crowds.

The Romans were expert builders and clever engineers. Their cities had luxurious public baths, arenas for public entertainment, libraries, and schools (although usually only the boys went to school). Some of the arenas were so large that more than 150,000 people at a time could watch the chariot racing!

10 THINGS TO SPOT

STONEMASONS Aksumite builders were skilled stonemasons. Stone blocks were carved to fit together tightly without the need for mortar or cement.

STELAE The most unusual Aksumite buildings are stone columns called "stelae." Stelae could weigh up to 176 tons and the tallest was an incredible 97 feet from ground to tip.

BURIAL TOMBS When members of the royal family died, they were buried in tombs beneath the stelae.

CROPS By building terraces on hillsides, the Aksumites could grow crops even on steep slopes.

COINS The Aksumites produced Africa's first gold and silver coins. These were the first in the world to include a Christian cross.

KINGDOM OF AKSUM (120 BC – 850 AD)

The Kingdom of Aksum was one of the greatest empires in African history and covered much of modern-day Ethiopia and parts of Eritrea, Djibouti, and Sudan. It was among the first great civilizations to convert to Christianity. Aksum's position on the shores of the Red Sea meant it was well placed to trade with other great empires of this time. These included Egypt, Rome, and India, making the king and his noblemen very rich.

Many of the people lived in towns, and archaeologists have found the remains of around a dozen large settlements. The Aksumites were efficient farmers who grew wheat and barley, and raised animals such as sheep, cattle, and camels.

 WRITING The Aksumites were also the first Africans to have a written language. It was called "Ge'ez."

 TEFF A special edible grain called "teff" grew well in this region, even when there was little rainfall.

 TREASURES African gold and emeralds were sold abroad in exchange for rare spices and silk.

 SALT Salt was valuable because it is essential for life. The Aksumites made it by allowing the hot sun to evaporate seawater held in shallow pools.

 THE TEN COMMANDMENTS Some people believe the original two stone tablets carved with the Biblical Ten Commandments lie buried somewhere in this region.

Historians still don't know what caused the empire to collapse. Some believe that climate change made it impossible to grow enough food for the large population. Another theory is that thousands of Aksumites died during the Plague of Justinian, an epidemic that killed nearly a quarter of all the people in the world.

MAYAN CIVILIZATION (200 – 900 AD)

The Mayan people lived in Mexico and in other parts of what we now call Central America. Instead of being one single group, the population was made up of separate tribes, clans, and families who spoke a variety of different languages. Individual cities were like small countries. Each had its own ruler who lived in a stone palace and was surrounded by rich noblemen, warriors, and priests. The cities traded with each other and their people shared many of the same traditions and cultures.

The most impressive buildings were giant stepped pyramids used for religious ceremonies. Some were designed with a temple on top for the priests to climb up to, but others belonged to the gods and no-one was allowed to even touch them.

10 THINGS TO SPOT

 SLAVES Mayan kings and nobles didn't walk anywhere but were carried from place to place by slaves.

 HATS Hats showed how important a person was. The larger the hat, the more important the wearer!

 FARMERS Most ordinary people worked hard from dawn to dusk, growing beans, tomatoes, hot chillies, and maize (corn).

 MAIZE Maize was ground into flour and used to make "tortilla" (a type of bread), porridge, and even drinks.

 TOOLS Metal was expensive so farmers carved their own stone tools.

 TATTOOS Married couples were often decorated with tattoos.

Most ordinary people lived in small huts made out of mud and thatch. Like the palaces and pyramids, these were often built on top of mounds to protect them from flooding.

CHOCOLATE The Maya were the first people to drink chocolate and thought cocoa beans were a delicious gift from the gods.

MUSIC Music and dancing were widely enjoyed but also formed part of some religious ceremonies.

MAKEUP Large noses were regarded as beautiful so rich Mayans sometimes used makeup to make their own noses look bigger.

CALENDAR PYRAMIDS The Mayans had a sophisticated calendar and built a pyramid with four sets of 91 steps. With one more on top this made a total of 365—one for each day of the year.

AZTEC EMPIRE (1345 – 1521 AD)

The Aztecs were warlike nomads who eventually settled down after conquering most of Mexico. Today, the remains of their largest city, Tenochtitlan, lies underneath the modern capital city of Mexico.

The city was built on an island surrounded by swamps. This provided good defense against attack, but there wasn't enough land to feed a population of around 200,000. To solve this problem, the Aztecs built large rectangular islands called chinampas or "floating gardens." These were around 300 feet long and were made by piling mud from the swamp onto giant rafts made of branches. To stop them drifting away, the raft corners were tied to willow trees growing in the swamp. Farmers paddled canoes from one island to the next, and grew beans, peppers, tomatoes, and flowers.

The empire was eventually destroyed by Spanish invaders. Thousands of Aztecs were killed in battle, while many others died after catching strange diseases from the newly arrived Europeans.

10 THINGS TO SPOT

COLORED FEATHERS Only the emperor was allowed to wear turquoise. Noblemen wore colored feathers to show how important they were. Wearing the wrong thing was punishable by death!

SCHOOL Teenage children had to go to school—even slaves. In most early civilizations, only the rich were educated and often only the boys.

WARRIORS Aztec men all trained as warriors. The empire grew by conquering neighboring tribes.

CRIMINALS Criminals could avoid punishment if they confessed to a crime before being caught. They could only do this once.

MARKET TRADING In markets, trade was mostly by barter, which means swapping one item for another.

ARRANGED MARRIAGE Marriages were arranged and most people did not get to choose their own partners.

TOOLS Because they didn't have iron or bronze, Aztecs made tools from bone, stone, or a type of volcanic glass called obsidian.

CALENDAR A giant stone calendar or Xiuhpohualli divided the year into 18 months, each made up of 20 days.

MUSIC Aztecs loved flutes, whistles, drums, and especially poetry. This passed from generation to generation but was rarely written down.

PATOLLI Patolli was a board game using dried beans as dice. Players moved six pieces across a board and the game involved skill and luck. It was extremely popular!

GALLERY OF FAMOUS FIGURES

Sometimes very little is known about the ordinary people who lived in many ancient civilizations. Thousands of years later, we don't even know their names or who they married. When we do know names, this is usually because they belonged to powerful kings or queens or to great military leaders who fought battles to expand the size of their empires by conquering neighboring countries.

Even people whose names are known can still be mysterious. Paintings and sculptures showing how they looked are not always accurate. Artists often depicted important men and women in an idealized form to make them look stronger and more handsome or more beautiful than they really were. Here is a collection of famous figures from throughout the ancient world.

MESOPOTAMIA

Gudea was a powerful Mesopotamian ruler from around 2144 BC. He married Ninalla, the daughter of a king.

INDUS VALLEY

The Dancing Girl is one of the best and most famous statues found in the Indus Valley, although her true identity is still a mystery.

EGYPT

Tutankhamun is one of the most famous Egyptian pharaohs and ruled the kingdom as a young boy. He was still a teenager when he died around 1323 BC, and his tomb was one of the richest ever found when it was discovered in 1922.

OLMEC

The most distinctive Olmec sculptures are giant human heads. They probably represent their rulers, but no-one knows any of their names.

CARTHAGE

Queen Dido (839–759 BC) is thought to have founded the Carthaginian Empire after being given a small piece of land in North Africa.

KINGDOM OF KUSH

Aspelta, who died in about 580 BC, ruled the kingdom for around 20 years. He had several wives, four of whom are buried beneath their own pyramids.

BABYLONIA

Nebuchadnezzar II (605–562 BC) built the major cities of the Neo-Babylonian Empire and may have been responsible for the famous Hanging Gardens.

PERSIA

Cyrus the Great (600–530 BC) was a formidable military commander whose skill made him the ruler of much of the ancient world.

GREECE

Alexander the Great (356–323 BC) spent almost his entire adult life fighting battles and winning wars. His empire spanned the ancient world and more than 20 cities were named in his honor.

QIN CHINA

Qin Shi Huang (259–210 BC) was the country's first ruler to call himself Emperor. His name is pronounced "chin" which may explain the country's English name, China.

XIONGNU EMPIRE

Modu (234–174 BC) was the founder of the Xiongnu Empire and seized the throne after killing his own father. He was supported by a strong army, who admired his bravery on the battlefield.

PARTHIAN EMPIRE

Artabanus V (died 224 BC) was the last ruler of an empire that lasted more than 400 years. He was killed in battle but his image has survived on many old coins.

ROME

Julius Caesar (100–44 BC) was a Roman politician and military general. He seized power, making himself dictator, but was killed by friends and rivals who feared he had become too powerful.

KINGDOM OF AKSUM

King Endubis (c. 270–300 AD) was the first African ruler to mint or make his own gold and silver coins.

MAYA

K'inich Janaab' Pakal (603–683 AD) was only 12 when he came to the throne. He ruled the Mayan Empire for a record 68 years and after his death was declared a god by his people.

AZTEC

Acamapichtli (died in 1395) was the first "tlatoani" (ruler) of the Aztecs. His name means "handful of reeds" and he preferred forming peaceful alliances with his neighbors rather than going to war.

CAN YOU FIND?

Take a look at the items below and see if you can remember which scene in the book they appear in. If you haven't seen them before, now is your chance to hunt them down by turning back to each action-packed scene for a second look.

Try using a magnifying glass to study the finer detail in each spread. You'll be surprised what else you missed the first time round.

SUNBATHING

WATCH OUT!

 BROKEN SWORD

 IN A BASKET

 CLIMBING UP

 CHASING GOATS

 PEEK-A-BOO

 GOLD!

 BROKEN STATUE

 CHEEKY MONKEY

 COLORFUL MASKS

 ON THE EDGE

 WINDSWEPT

 PEACOCK

 YOGA

 FALLING OVER

 CHASING BIRDS

 SLITHERING SNAKE

 PET GIRAFFE

 HOLDING ON

 RIDING CROCODILES

 PET LEOPARD

 CARPET CARRYING

 FLOATING

 A PIG'S BEST FRIEND

 FLYING THROUGH THE AIR!

 TOILET TIME

OOPS!

GOING HIGHER

TEAMWORK

DIP YOUR TOES IN

HUNTING

RUNNING AWAY

MONKEY TIME

GALLOPING

PICNIC

TIME TO READ

CARRYING A CHICKEN

HI!

OUCH!

PEEK-A-BOO LEOPARD

PARROT PALS

PET TURTLE

SITTING UP HIGH

GOODS EXCHANGE

HANG ON!

BURNING BOTTOM

DIVING IN

SORE TOE!

CHILLING OUT IN A HAMOCK

YEE-HAW!

HUG

HAVING A DRINK

SNAKE HANDLER

FISHING

YAWN

DAYDREAMING

ANSWERS

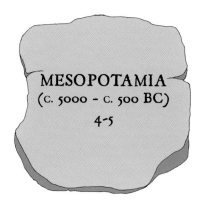

MESOPOTAMIA
(C. 5000 – C. 500 BC)
4-5

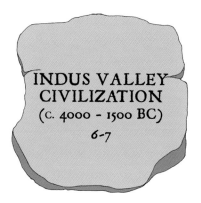

INDUS VALLEY CIVILIZATION
(C. 4000 – 1500 BC)
6-7

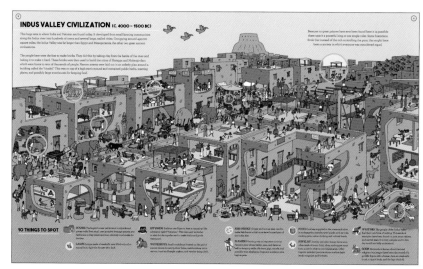

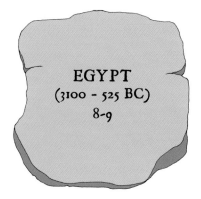

EGYPT
(3100 – 525 BC)
8-9

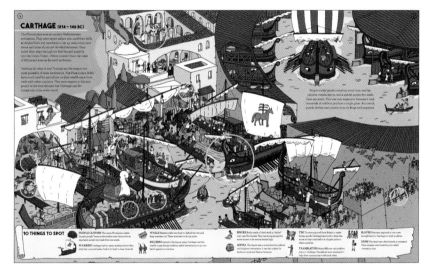

ANSWERS

NEO-
BABYLONIAN
EMPIRE
(c. 626 - 539 BC)
16-17

PERSIAN
EMPIRE
(c. 553 - 330 BC)
18-19

GREECE
(550 BC - 31 BC)
20-21

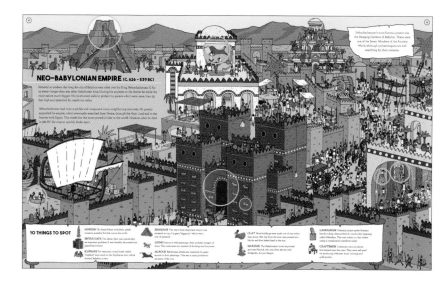

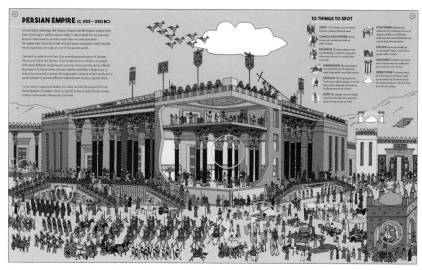

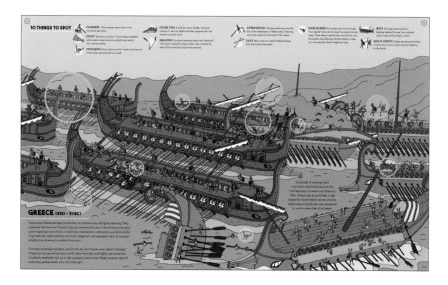

QIN DYNASTY
(221 BC – 206 BC)

22–23

XIONGNU EMPIRE
(209 BC – 46 AD)

24–25

PARTHIAN EMPIRE
(247 BC – 224 AD)

26–27

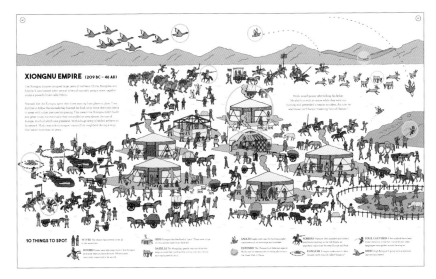

ANSWERS

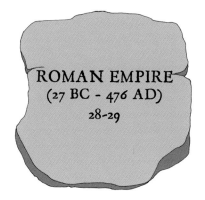

ROMAN EMPIRE
(27 BC – 476 AD)
28-29

KINGDOM OF AKSUM
(120 BC – 850 AD)
30-31

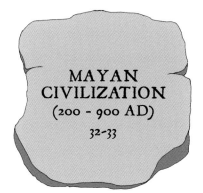

MAYAN CIVILIZATION (200 - 900 AD)
32-33

AZTEC EMPIRE (1345 - 1521 AD)
34-35

TIMELINE

50,000-25,000 BC
People begin wearing clothes for the first time. The oldest known garment is the Tarkhan Dress which was found in an Egyptian tomb. The world's oldest pants were found in China.

10,000 BC
The first boats are constructed by hollowing out tree trunks using hand tools made of stone.

9000-8000 BC
Organized agriculture begins in the Middle East. This alters the way people live because tribes no longer have to move from place to place to find enough food to survive.

5000-3500 BC
Glass is made for the first time in what is now Iraq. Some people believe that it may have been discovered by accident when ordinary sand melted close to a campfire.

2000 BC
Water-raising devices like the shaduf improve agriculture in the Middle East through better irrigation. By growing more crops, societies were able to expand. Villages grew to become towns and large towns became cities.

2500 BC
Egyptians produce papyrus, an early version of paper. It was made from a 13-feet-tall weed which grew along the banks of the river Nile.

2560 BC
The Great Pyramid is completed in Egypt. It took more than 20 years to move 2.5 million stone blocks into place.

3500 BC
The invention of the potter's wheel. It took hundreds of years before anyone thought of using it for transport and the first vehicle to use something similar was probably a Greek wheelbarrow.

1700 BC
Semites of the eastern Mediterranean develop the alphabet. The oldest alphabet still in use is thought to be Hebrew, which is found in Jewish prayerbooks.

1000 BC
Iron is widely used for making tools and weapons in many parts of the world. Metal tools worked better than stone ones and soldiers with metal weapons could fight more effectively than those without.

850 BC
The oldest calendar still in use is the Jewish calendar, which dates from around this time. Calendars and a better understanding of the seasons helped make agriculture more efficient so that more food could be produced.

400 BC
The Chinese experiment with flying kites. Some were flown as toys, but they could also be used for testing the wind, measuring distances, sending messages over long distances, and even lifting men into the air!

105 AD
The first real paper is manufactured in China. It rapidly became stronger, thinner, and cheaper to produce than Egyptian papyrus.

50 BC
The Romans perfect the water wheel. These were used to convert flowing water into power, and to irrigate crops to produce more food.

150-100 BC
The first clockwork machines appear in Greece. The oldest, the Antikythera Mechanism, was like an early computer. It was used to predict the positions of the stars.

300 BC
In China, magnetic stones are used to make primitive compasses. Understanding which direction is north makes it far easier for explorers to navigate and find their way around the world.

600 AD
Windmills are invented in the Middle East. Generating power from wind made it possible to grind grain to flour and to pump water more efficiently than in the past.

700-900 AD
The Chinese invent gunpowder which is used for fireworks and primitive weapons. The weapons eventually revolutionized the way wars were fought, although early weapons were unreliable and often killed the people using them.

1000 AD
Work begins to construct the African city of Great Zimbabwe, an important religious and trading center. The people of Great Zimbabwe probably worshipped Mwari, the most important god in the Shona religion.

1206 AD
A Persian inventor produces a flushing hand-washing machine. This is later adapted to produce the modern flushing toilet. Queen Elizabeth I of England was given one of these in the 16th century but ordinary people had to wait another 200 years.

GLOSSARY

Here are some words you might come across when you're reading about the ancient world.

ADOBE
A hard building material made by drying earth, water, and straw or dung.

AFTERLIFE
In some religions, the place where a person's soul goes after death.

AGORA
A central, open space in ancient cities where the public could gather and important business could be carried out.

AGRICULTURE
Any form of farming. Agriculture allowed ancient peoples to settle in one place and grow food.

AQUEDUCT
A channel for moving water across long distances.

ASTRONOMY
The study of stars and planets. Ancient astronomers studied how these moved over time, which helped to make calendars and maps.

BARTER
A system of trade where goods are swapped, rather than bought with money.

BALLISTA
An ancient Roman siege weapon that could fire stones or bolts long distances.

BITUMEN
Sticky black substance used in ancient buildings to hold bricks together.

BLOOMERY
A hot forge used to produce iron that could be shaped into tools and weapons.

CATAPHRACT
Parthian horseback soldier. Both the soldier and horse were covered in heavy armor.

CHARIOT
A horse-pulled cart driven by a charioteer, used in warfare and raced for sport.

CHINAMPA
Small, artificial islands used by the Aztecs and Mayans to grow food on bodies of water.

CUNEIFORM
A type of writing made by carving markings into soft clay with a blunt tool.

GER
A round tent used by Central Asian nomads, including the Xiongnu.

HIEROGLYPHIC
Ancient Egyptian writing that used small pictures instead of words.

INCENSE
Natural substances that produce a strong fragrance when burned, often used for religious purposes.

INSULA
A type of apartment block in ancient Roman cities. It translates literally as "island."

IRRIGATION
Bringing water to farmland to help crops grow, usually by digging channels.

JAVELIN
A spear that could be thrown. Javelins were used in battle and in sport.

KILN
A large oven in which clay is baked and hardened.

KUPHAR
A round boat from ancient Mesopotamia. It could be moved by rowing or with a long pole.

KURGAN
In Central Asia and northern Europe, a mound of earth marking a grave.

KYBERNETES
The Greek word for "helmsman," the person in charge of directing and steering a ship.

MERCENARY
A professional soldier available for hire.

MOSAIC
A type of artwork made from lots of tiny pieces of ceramic, stone, or glass.

NOMAD
A person who moves from place to place without settling. Nomadic people often lived in tribes.

PAPYRUS
A material made from dried plants turned into sheets, used for writing or drawing on.

PHARAOH
What ancient Egyptians called their king or queen.

PHILOSOPHY
The study of knowledge, reality, and existence.

PYRAMID
A building with a wide base that narrows to a pointed top, typically built as a tomb.

RELIEF
A carving, somewhere between a picture and a sculpture, where the design sits farther out than its background.

RESERVOIR
A natural or artificial lake used for storing fresh water.

SATRAP
In ancient Persia, this was a governor of any of the empire's many provinces.

SEXAGESIMAL
A counting system used by the ancient Mesopotamians.

SCRIBE
A person whose job was to write or copy out important documents.

SHEARING
A naval warfare tactic used by the ancient Greeks. The crew used their oars to break those of their enemy.

SLASH-AND-BURN
A farming method in which forests and plants are ripped up and burned to make room for crops.

STATUETTE
A small statue.

STELA
An upright slab of stone or clay with writing on it.

TABLET
A small slab, typically made of clay, that could be written on.

TEFF
A cereal grown in eastern Africa.

TERRACOTTA
A material made of fired clay that can be used for building or decoration.

TESTUDO
An ancient Roman military formation. Soldiers would stand close together, holding their shields above and in front for protection.

TLATOANI
What the Aztecs called their kings. Queens were called cihuātlahtoāni.

TRIREME
An ancient Greek naval vessel with sails, three rows of oars, and a ram.

XIUHPOHUALLI
The Aztec calendar: 365 days divided into 18 months.

ZIGGURAT
A structure with several terraces on top of each other, each slightly smaller than the one beneath.

This edition published in 2021 by Chartwell Books,
an imprint of The Quarto Group,
142 W. 36th Street, 4th Floor, new York, NY 10018, USA
T (212) 779-4972 F (212) 779-6058 www.QuartoKnows.com

Chartwell titles are also available at discount for retail, wholesale, promotional, and bulk purchase. For details, contact the Special Sales Manager by email at specialsales@quarto.com or by mail at The Quarto Group, Attn: Special Sales Manager, 100 Cummings Center Suite 265D, Beverly, MA 01915, USA.

ISBN: 978-0-7858-3970-5

Designed by Myrto Dimitrakoulia
Edited by Claire Grace
Published by Georgia Amson-Bradshaw
Production by Chris Tucker

3 5 7 9 8 6 4 2

Not for individual sale.

Printed in China